THE HOUSE BOOK
A RECORD OF OUR HOME

by

Liz Throop

Hugh Lauter Levin Associates Inc., New York

Distributed by

Macmillan Publishing Company

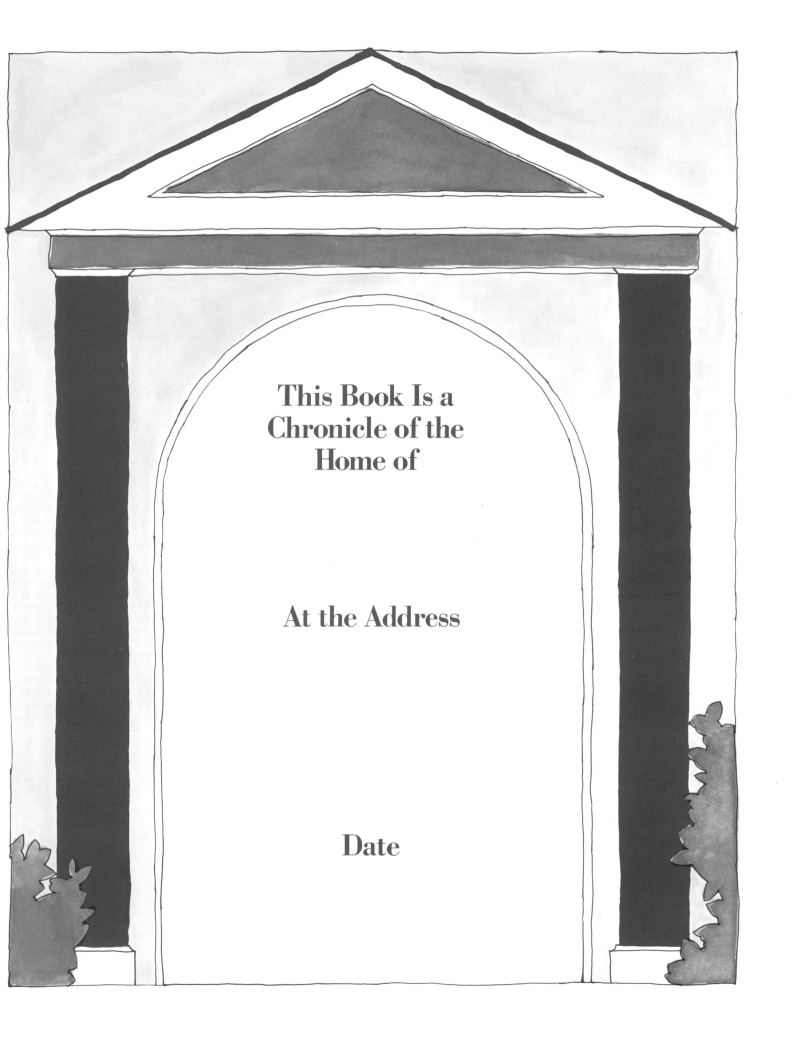

This Book Is a
Chronicle of the
Home of

At the Address

Date

Homeowners have never left their homes unaltered. They have always decorated, redecorated, repaired, expanded, fine-tuned and updated them. If your house is old, you may at times find yourself becoming an archaeologist, as you uncover old toys in the garden, fireplaces behind paneling and ancient wallpaper behind switchplates. You may come to realize that the structure and its many details are of both historic and practical value.

If your home is newly built, it is also unique in its relation to the land it is on and to you. It is sure to evolve in a singular way.

We can only speculate how energy-saving devices, microcircuits and new ideas about leisure and family will eventually affect our homes. Whatever the trends for the future, recording information about your house and the changes it undergoes will make this book a useful planning and reference tool. You and future owners of the house will find it invaluable for locating the electric meter, identifying plantings and appreciating all the work that went into making your house a home.

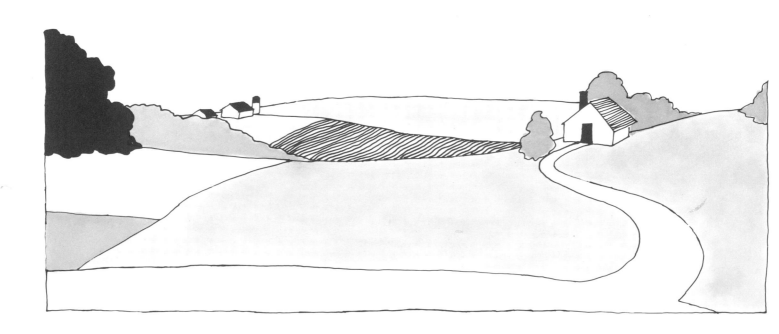

Name of Community

Use of Land Previous to Our Home

Geographic and Geologic Features of the Land

Surveys

land lot number   district   county   plat book   date of survey

Previous Owners of the House and Land

name   dates

General Architectural Style

Original Construction

date foundation laid   date roof installed   date of first occupancy

Architects, Engineers & Builders of Original House

photos of
house during
construction

description/date:

photos
of owners

description/date:

Residents of Our Home

name   dates of occupancy

Special Guests in Our Home

name   dates

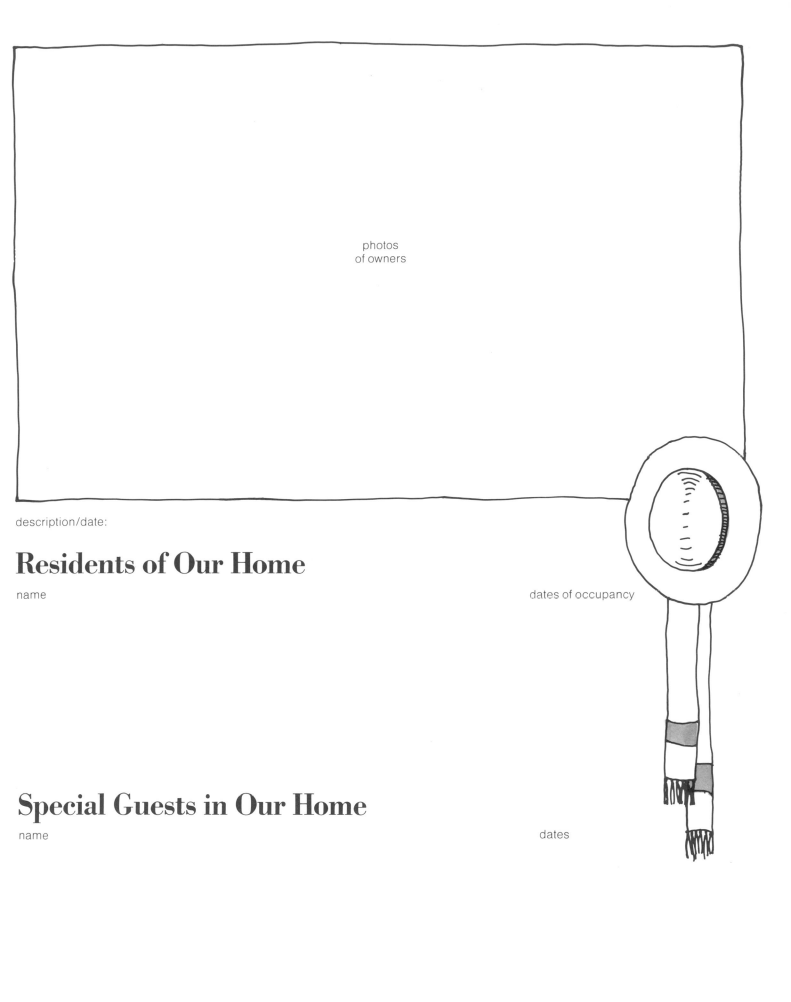

Major Restorations of Original House

description   work done by   date

Major Additions and Renovations

description   work done by   date

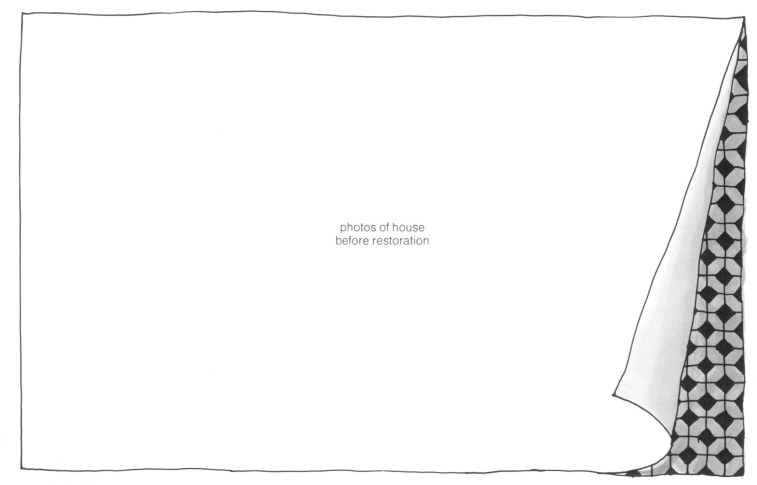

photos of house
before restoration

description/date:

Elements Removed or Replaced

description   work done by   date

photos of house
after restoration

description/date:

Plan of the First Floor

 door    wall   window   fireplace   refrigerator   stove   sink

Plan of the Second Floor

electric outlet   light   closet   toilet   sink   tub   stairs

Floor Plans of Attic & Cellar

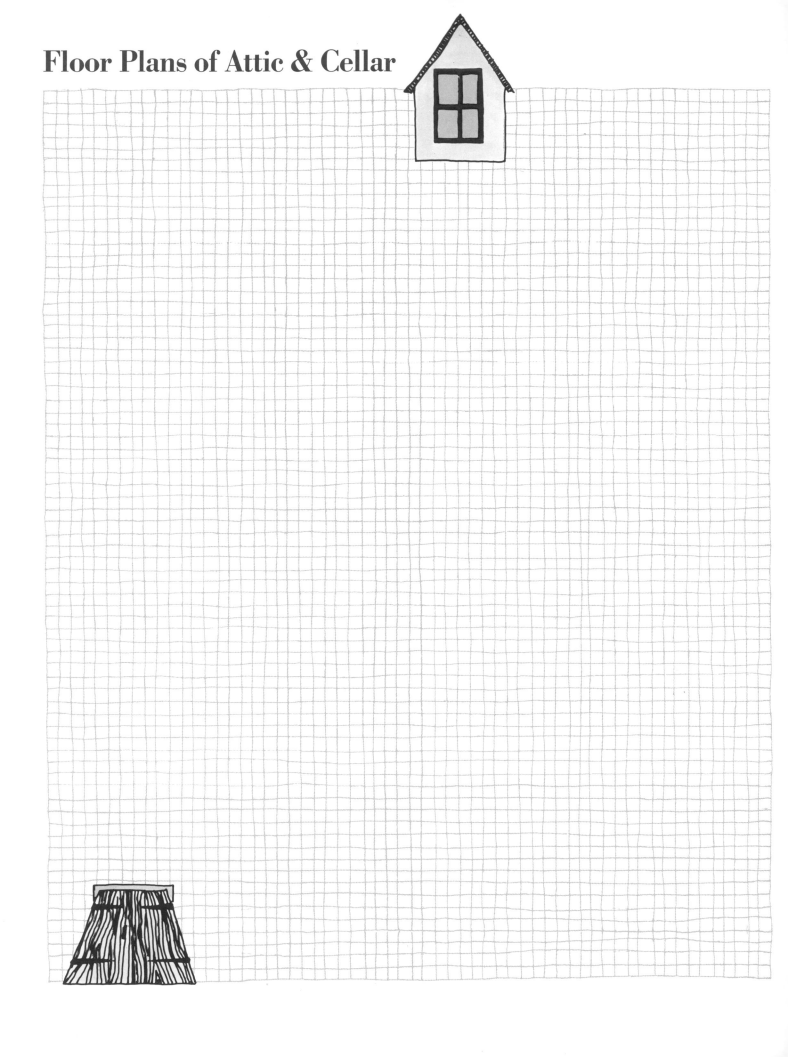

Carpenters

name   work done   date

Electricians

name   work done   date

Plumbers

name   work done   date

Masons & Bricklayers

name   work done   date

Roofers

name   work done   date

Painters & Paperers

name   work done   date

Decorators

name   work done   date

Other Contractors

name   work done   date

Carpet Installers

name   work done   date

Chimney Sweeps & Inspectors

name   work done   date

Drapery Makers & Upholsterers

name   work done   date

Driveway Pavers

name   work done   date

Exterminators

name   work done   date

Gutter Cleaners

name   work done   date

Housekeeping & Cleaning Services

name   work done   date

Landscapers & Groundskeepers

name   work done   date

Locksmiths

name   work done   date

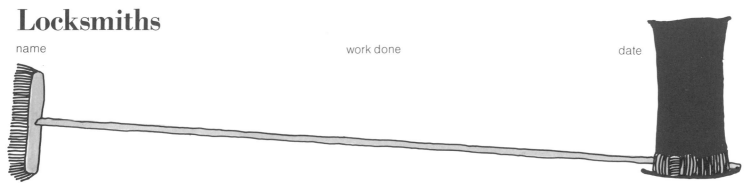

Doors, Doorknobs, Hinges, Locks and Bells

item   manufacturer/model

Windows and Screens

item   manufacturer/model

photos of
interior details

description/date:

Fireplaces, Screens, Grates & Andirons

item

manufacturer/model

Molding, Trim & Decorative Plasterwork

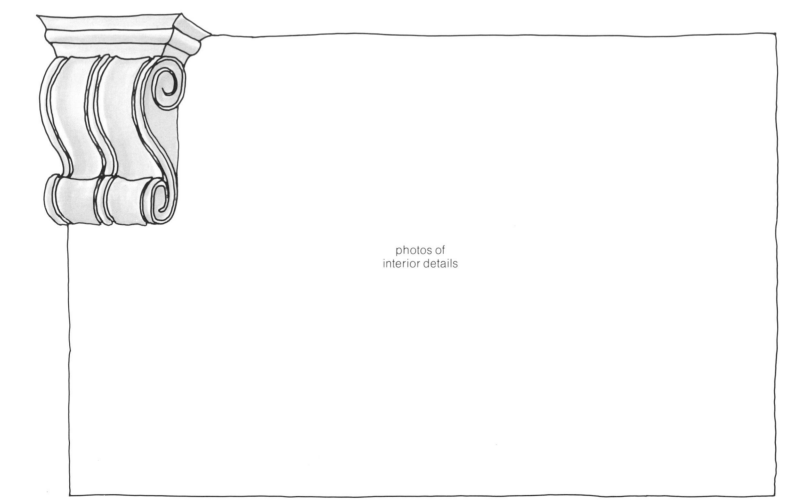

photos of
interior details

Molding, Trim & Decorative Plasterwork

description/date:

Light Fixtures

room	manufacturer/model	special bulbs	source

Wiring

fusebox location   meter location   number of amps   date serviced or updated

Switchplates & Rheostats

item   manufacturer/model

Fuses or Circuits

switch 1	switch 6
switch 2	switch 7
switch 3	switch 8
switch 4	switch 9
switch 5	switch 10

TV Cable

name of system   installer & servicer   date serviced

Intercom

manufacturer/model   installer & servicer   unit location   date serviced

Phone Lines

name of company   installer & servicer   date serviced

Phones

manufacturer/model/color   location

Flooring

room   description   source   date refinished

Ceilings

room   description   source   date resurfaced

Smoke Alarm

manufacturer/model   battery replacement date

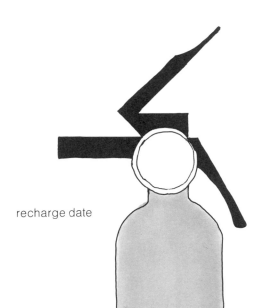

Fire Extinguishers

manufacturer/model   location   recharge date

Security System

manufacturer/model   location of controls   installer   date serviced

Water Supply

pump manufacturer/model   filter manufacturer/model   well location   date serviced

cutoff location   cutoff tool location   meter location

Water Heater

manufacturer/model   location   date serviced

Sewer or Septic System

installer & servicer   clean-out plug location   tank location   date serviced

Gas Lines

installer & servicer   meter location   cutoff location   date serviced

Furnace

installer & servicer   manufacturer/model   location   date serviced

Radiators & Registers

manufacturer/model   location   date serviced

Thermostat

manufacturer/model   location   date serviced

Air Conditioners & Fans

installer & servicer   manufacturer/model   location   date serviced

Paint

room	manufacturer/color/number	alkyd/latex	gloss	date painted

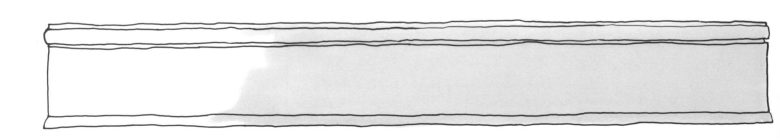

Paint Samples

Wallpaper

room	manufacturer/style/color	square feet required	date papered

Stains, Seals & Finishes

room	manufacturer/color	date applied

Wallpaper Samples

Diagram of Kitchen

sink

range

refrigerator

dishwasher

counters

overhead cabinets

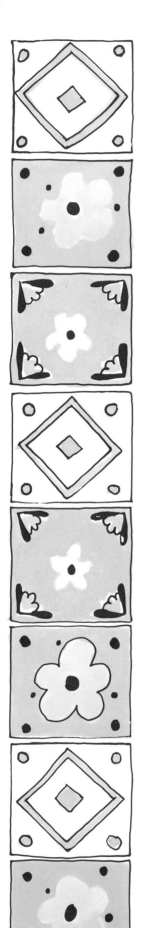

Kitchen Cabinets

manufacturer/model/color   source   date installed

Tiles & Laminates

manufacturer/model/color   source   date installed

Stove Range & Hood

manufacturer/model/color   source   date installed

Ovens

manufacturer/model/color   source   date installed

Dishwasher

manufacturer/model/color   source   date installed

Refrigerator

manufacturer/model/color   source   date installed

Trash Compactor

manufacturer/model/color   source   date installed

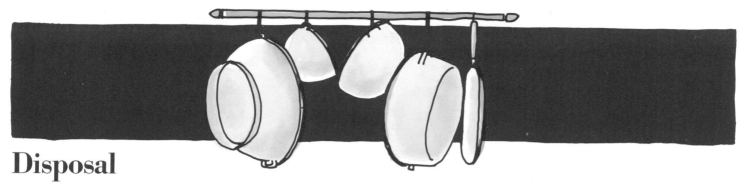

Disposal

manutacturer/model/color source date installed

Sink & Sink Fixtures

manufacturer/model/color source date installed

Kitchen Accessories

item manufacturer/model/color source description

Master Bath – Sink, Tub & Toilet

item   manufacturer/model/color   source   date installed

Faucets, Handles & Showerheads

item   manufacturer/model   source   date installed

Drapes, Tiles & Laminates

item   manufacturer/model/color   source   date installed

Heaters & Fans

manufacturer/model   source   date installed

Second Bath–Fixtures

item   manufacturer/model/color   source   date installed

Drapes, Tiles & Laminates

item   manufacturer/model/color   source   date installed

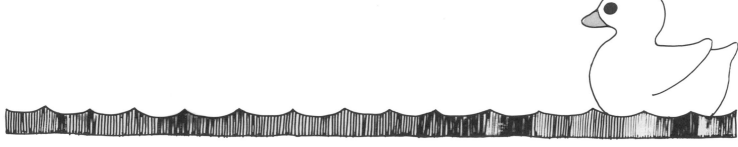

Guest Bath–Fixtures

item   manufacturer/model/color   source   date installed

Drapes, Tiles & Laminates

item   manufacturer/model/color   source   date installed

Workshop/Studio Fixtures

item   manufacturer/model/color   source   date installed

Washer

manufacturer/model/color   source

date installed   date serviced

Dryer

manufacturer/model/color   source

date installed   date serviced

Bookshelves
location   description

Cedar Storage
location   description

Laundry Storage
location   description

Linen Storage
location   description

Recreational Equipment Storage
location   description

Safe
location   description

Seasonal Decoration Storage
location   description

Tool Storage
location   description

Wine Storage
location   description

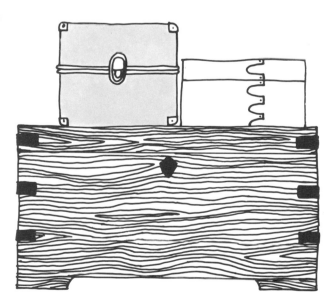

Living Room Furnishings

photos of
furnishings

description/date:

Dining Room Furnishings

item	manufacturer/model/color	source	date purchased

Den Furnishings

item	manufacturer/model/color	source	date purchased

Master Bedroom Furnishings

item	manufacturer/model/color	source	date purchased

Bedroom Furnishings

item	manufacturer/model/color	source	date purchased

photos of
furnishings

description/date:

Bedroom Furnishings

| item | manufacturer/model/color | source | date purchased |

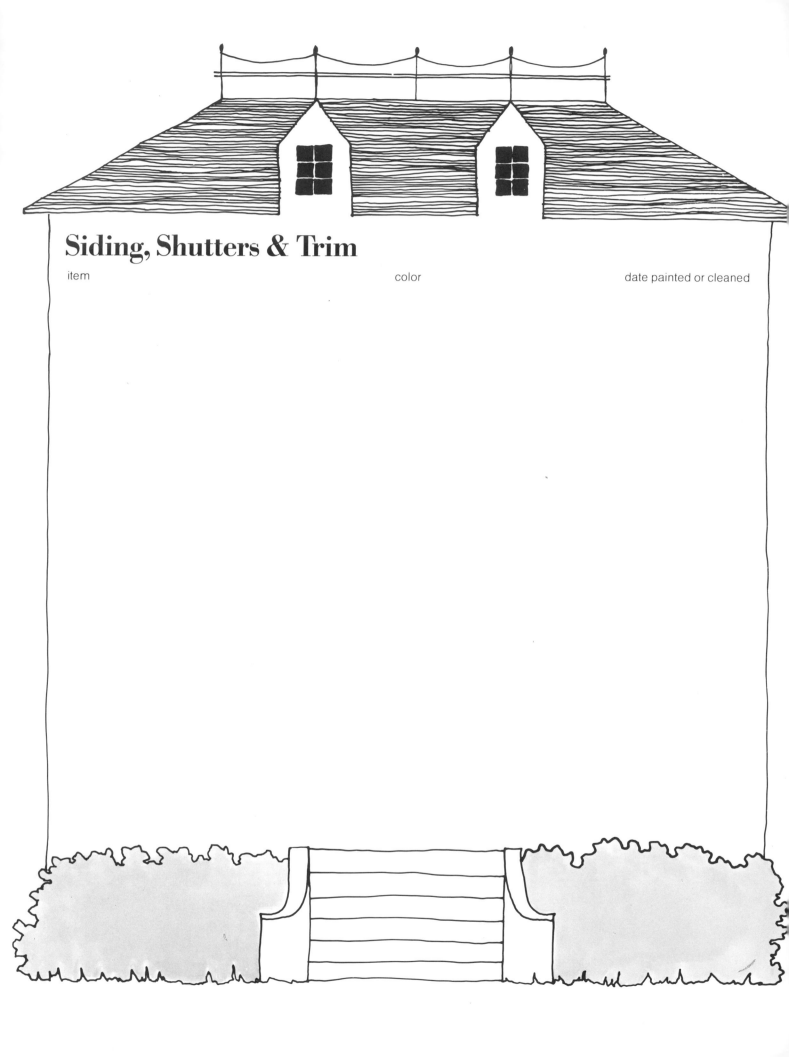

Siding, Shutters & Trim

item   color   date painted or cleaned

Vents, Awnings & Gutters

item   manufacturer/model/color   date cleaned or repaired

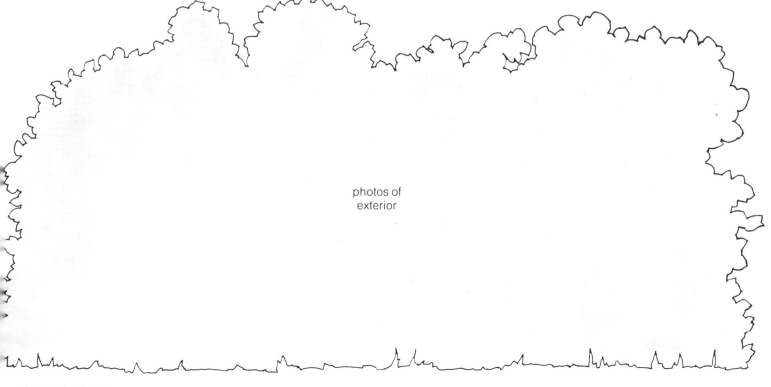

photos of
exterior

description/date:

Roof

material   work done   date repaired or replaced

Chimney

material   work done   date work done

Porches & Patios

material   work done   date repainted or repaired

Garages, Sheds & Other Outbuildings

description	material	work done	date work done

Fences, Gates & Security

description	material	work done	date work done

Outdoor Lights

manufacturer/model/color	source	special bulbs

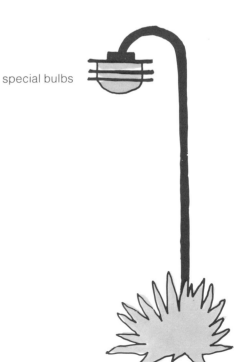

Pools, Tubs & Ponds

description   maintenance performed   maintenance dates

Driveways, Walkways & Embankments

description   location

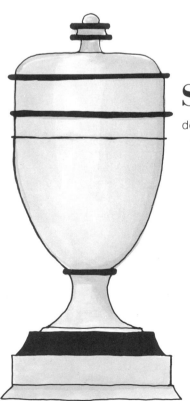

Statuary & Fountains

description   location   date installed

Outdoor Furniture, Grills & Playground Equipment

item   manufacturer/model/color   date purchased

Mailbox & Street Number Sign

item   manufacturer/model/color   date installed

Outdoor Seasonal
Lights & Decorations

description   years displayed

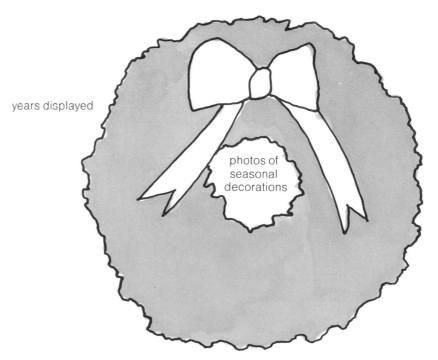

photos of
seasonal
decorations

description/date:

Plan of Yard

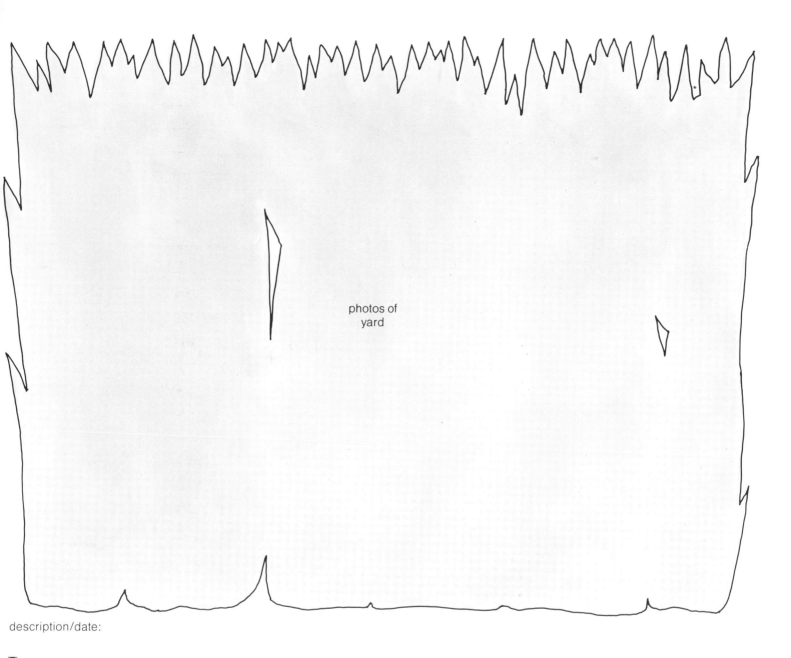

photos of
yard

description/date:

Lawn

grass type   fertilization date   date & description of other maintenance

Trees

| type of tree | location | approximate age | date & description of maintenance |

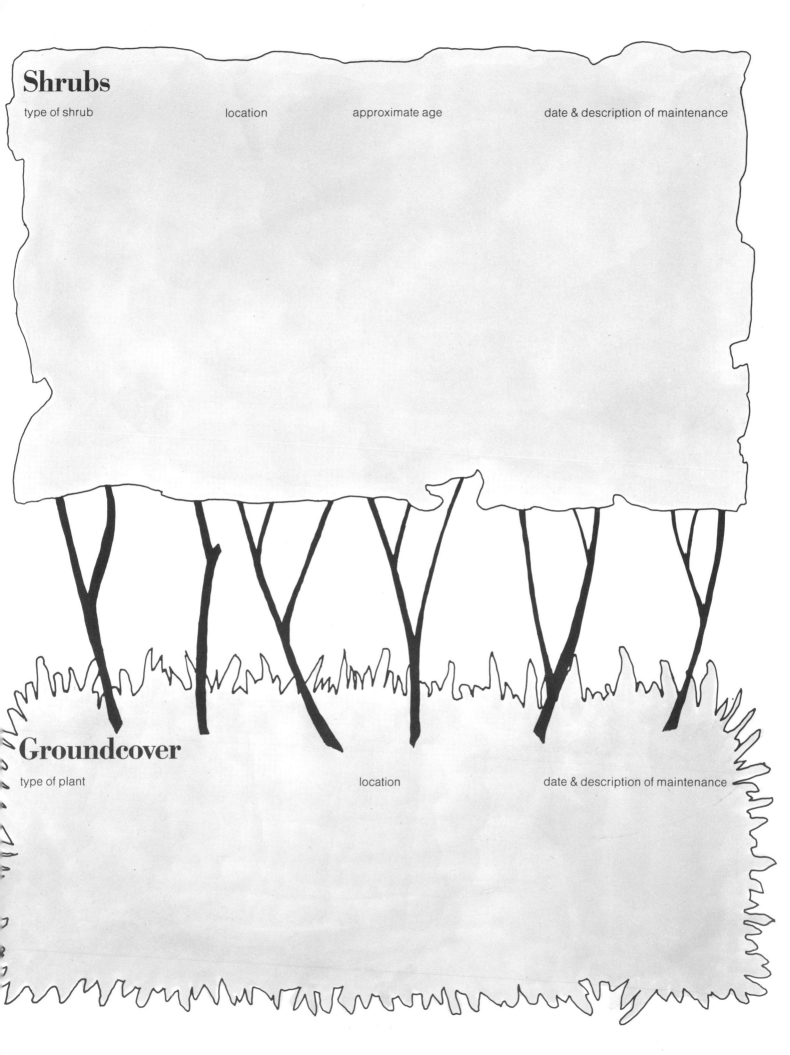

Shrubs

type of shrub location approximate age date & description of maintenance

Groundcover

type of plant location date & description of maintenance

Spring Flowers

type	source	location	maintenance	date planted

Summer Flowers

type	source	location	maintenance	date planted

Fall Flowers

type	source	location	maintenance	date planted

Winter Flowers

type	source	location	maintenance	date planted

photos of
flowers

description/date:

Spring Vegetables & Herbs

type	source	location	maintenance	date planted

Summer Vegetables & Herbs

type	source	location	maintenance	date planted

Fall Vegetables & Herbs

type   source   location   maintenance   date planted

Winter Vegetables & Herbs

type   source   location   maintenance   date planted

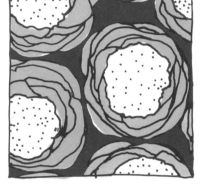

photos of
vegetables

description/date:

Wildflowers, Mushrooms & Other Indigenous Plants

type   location   date seen

more photos
of garden

description/date:

Birds Seen

type   location   date seen

Other Wildlife

type   location   date seen

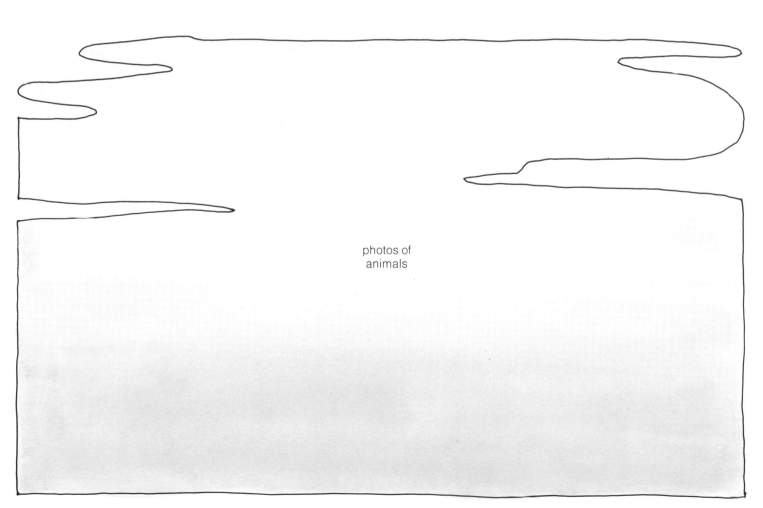

photos of
animals

description/date:

Neighboring Houses

style   location   date built

Nearby Parks

name   location

Local Landmarks

description   location

Schools

name location

Polling Place

location voting districts

Houses of Worship

name location

Community Festivals & Fairs

description   location   dates

Sport & Country Clubs

name   description   location

Civic Groups

name   description   location

Favorite Shops & Restaurants

name   description   location

Stories About Our Home

Stories About Our Home

Important Phone Numbers

fire _____

police _____

electric company _____

phone company _____

gas company _____

waterworks _____

insurance agent _____

neighbors _____

_____

sanitation _____

snow removal _____

carpenter _____

electrician _____

plumber _____

roofer _____

painter _____

paper hanger _____

decorator _____

carpet installer _____

drapery maker _____

upholsterer _____

locksmith/security system servicer _____

housekeeper _____

gardener _____

gutter cleaner _____

chimney sweep _____

tree surgeon _____

septic service _____

exterminator _____

appliance inspectors and repairers _____

_____

_____

other contractors _____

_____

_____